I0257892

THIS IS A PARRAGON BOOK

© Parragon 1996

Parragon
13-17 Avonbridge Trading Estate
Atlantic Road, Avonmouth,
Bristol, BS11 9QD

Produced by The Templar Company plc,
Pippbrook Mill, London Road, Dorking
Surrey RH4 1JE

Designed by Mark Kingsley Monks

Printed and bound in Great Britain

ISBN 0 75252 062 8

THE
Jam Pandas'
FIRST BOOK OF
Shapes

ILLUSTRATED BY STEPHANIE BOEY
WRITTEN BY CLAIRE STEEDEN

PARRAGON

All the Jam Pandas are excited, especially Baby Jim Jam. It is his birthday today.

The Jam Pandas are
busy getting ready for
his birthday party.

They have each
made something
special to eat.

Grandma has made jam tarts. They are each shaped like a **circle**. She is covered in flour! **Can you find some more circle shapes in the picture?**

circle

Pa has made pieces
of toast.
They are each shaped
like a **square**.
He puts them on
the table.
**What else can you see
that is square-shaped?**

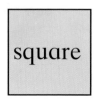

square

Peaches has made jam sandwiches. They are each shaped like a **triangle**. She has gone outside to play while she waits for the party to start. **Can you find some more triangles in the picture?**

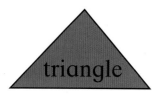

triangle

Ma has made a
raspberry jelly. It is
shaped like an **oval**.
She is in her bedroom
getting dressed for
the party.
**Can you see any oval
shapes in Ma's room?**

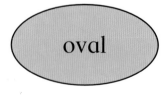

oval

Big Bamboo has baked
a birthday cake.
It is shaped like a
rectangle.
He is making
Jim Jam a card.
**Can you find some
more rectangle shapes
in the picture?**

rectangle

Plum has made some chocolates.
They are each shaped like a **diamond**.
He is wrapping Jim Jam's present.
It is a puzzle.
Can you find some more diamond shapes in the picture?

diamond

Aunt Apricot has made some biscuits. They are each shaped like a **star**.
She brings them with her in a star-shaped tin. **What other star shapes can you see in the picture?**

star

It's time for the party to start and the games to begin!

The Jam Pandas sit down to eat the lovely food they have made.
Can you find all the different shapes in this picture?

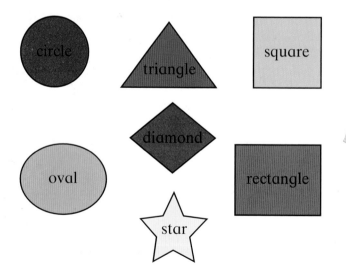

circle

triangle

square

diamond

oval

rectangle

star

Titles in this series include: